Learning Mathematics in the Nursery: Desirable Approaches

The Early Childhood Mathematics Group

The statement below is taken from *Nursery Education: Desirable Outcomes for Children's Learning on Entering Compulsory Education* (SCAA, 1996).

It is a very condensed summary of the mathematical learning which takes place during the first years of a child's life and needs considerable unwrapping and interpretation in the light of good early years educational practice. Although good practice is referred to in the SCAA document, we feel that there might be a strong temptation to target the mathematical 'outcomes' as separate short-term goals, rather than to consider children's mathematical education as an integrated and very individual experience.

> **66** *These outcomes cover important aspects of mathematical understanding and provide the foundation for numeracy. They focus on achievement through practical activities and on using and understanding language in the development of simple mathematical ideas.*
>
> *Children use mathematical language, such as circle, in front of, bigger than and more, to describe shape, position, size and quantity. They recognise and recreate patterns. They are familiar with number rhymes, songs, stories, counting games and activities. They compare, sort, match, order, sequence and count using everyday objects. They recognise and use numbers to 10 and are familiar with larger numbers from their everyday lives. They begin to use their developing mathematical understanding to solve problems. Through practical activities children understand and record numbers, begin to show awareness of number operations, such as addition and subtraction, and begin to use the language involved.* **99**

NURSERY EDUCATION: DESIRABLE OUTCOMES FOR CHILDREN'S LEARNING ON ENTERING COMPULSORY EDUCATION, page 3 (SCAA, 1996)

Contents

Starting with the child

Young children learning

As adults we need to be aware of how children learn and develop. Most useful learning at the nursery stage arises from play, which allows children to develop mathematical understanding and gain confidence in their abilities almost as a by-product of having fun.

Anyone who has worked with children of this age will know that they have their own ideas about what they want. They are capable of great concentration, unquenchable curiosity, wonderful imagination and seemingly irrational determination. These qualities will help them learn if we can manage to capture their imagination and attention by providing a stimulating and well-balanced environment.

Children as individuals

Education at this age should draw upon the experiences that children have already had at home. Each child has had different experiences, which means that they all have their own starting points and needs. Getting a feel for children's experience of home life will help you to recognise influences in their learning.

Children progress at different rates. Some children find learning easy, and need broad and challenging situations to deepen their understanding; others require a lot of support. All children, however, need to meet mathematical ideas in many different situations; and to meet them at a level which suits them.

In order to develop children's mathematical learning in an informal and enjoyable way, the adult's planning and specific use of mathematical language is vital.

The teacher drew a circle for each child, and they turned these into pictures. Frances, aged 4½, drew 'People dancing round a pond'

Getting ready for sums

The mathematical experiences we provide for children must be meaningful for them.

Let us look at a 'sum' such as 5 – 2 = 3. To us as adults it is a simple number statement which can be applied to many situations (earn £5, spend £2; buy 5 buns and 2 get eaten; I've got 5 children and you've got 2, which means I've got 3 more than you). But for most young children it is just a group of symbols with little meaning.

To develop mental pictures of number situations, children need a rich variety of practical and visual experiences. These include:

● working with number stories and rhymes that involve 'adding' and 'taking away' (for example, repeat the rhyme 'Ten little seagulls flying low; two said, "Sorry boys, I must go"' and allow children enough time to work out the number of seagulls left)

● practical experience (for example, getting three more spoons for the group)

This will help them to develop both the ideas and the language of addition and subtraction.

Children then need to meet and work with number symbols. Examples are: finding a wooden numeral that matches their age, making a birthday card for a friend, or reading a recipe to see how many cups of flour to use.

Gradually, as these experiences come together, children will get to the stage where they are ready to meet symbols such as '+' and '–' to describe the situations they are familiar with — but this is some way ahead for most nursery children.

Starting where the child is

It is very important to find out what the child knows and is interested in and to use this as a starting point for activities. We need to:

● observe what children do and say as they play, and note their responses to the activities we provide

● use this information to design further activities and challenges which are appropriate to the children's needs

● use a flexible approach

● build on experiences children bring with them (if it snows, drop the plans for the morning: make snow people and talk about which one is tallest, fattest, widest; if a child has visited the fair, build roundabouts from blocks and talk about their shapes, and so on)

Thomas (4 years 8 months) knocked down 6 skittles; he tallied the score, then drew the skittles

The adult's role

Positive attitudes matter

Part of the adult's role is to help the children to develop positive attitudes to mathematics. This means the adult needs to value the experiences and knowledge children bring to the nursery, and develop a partnership with parents and carers. As adults we also need to value the way we use mathematics in our daily lives, and to share this with the children.

Providing a rich environment

The teaching adult needs to set up a mathematically rich environment where children will experience mathematical ideas in a purposeful way. There are two aspects to this: what we provide, and what we say and do.

What to provide

● resources for the room which relate to mathematics: calculators and large handleable numerals; dice and dominoes; construction materials; examples of regular and irregular shapes (2D and 3D); instruments like weighing scales, clocks, calendars and watches; rulers, tape measures and height charts; mathematical games and puzzles; a collection of interesting objects such as leaves, or 'round things'; books containing mathematical ideas . . .

● interactive displays of mathematical interest (portraits of the children showing their ages; a collection of square things; number friezes . . .)

● stimulating, varied and challenging activities relevant to the children's lives: "Have we got enough biscuits for everyone?" "How many steps to the slide?"

● an insight into how we as adults use mathematical skills as part of organising and planning the day — show children the charts we make, let them see us counting the class or looking at the calendar or clock . . .

● situations in which children can take responsibility — helping to count the chairs, lay the table, or tidy up . . .

Using mental imagery

Pleasure and enjoyment

Using everyday mathematics

Investigating the environment

Trying, making mistakes and refining skills

EXPERIENCES TO BE FOSTERED

Autonomy and self-responsibility

Awareness of self, family and community

Exploring real objects in real situations

EXPLORATORY AND IMAGINATIVE PLAY

Understanding how children learn and the nature of mathematics; using mathematical language with the children

ADULT SUPPORT

Observing the child's responses and recording, then planning for the future

Communicating with parents/carers and sharing knowledge of the child's home

Providing
● a practical learning environment
● sensitive intervention
● support for thinking, talking and reflection

This diagram shows all the different ingredients we need to help children learn mathematically

Things to say

● use mathematical language with children and encourage them to use it too: "Have you got more than me?". Value their own spontaneous mathematical language: "Mine's a pointy one"

● encourage questioning, thinking and discussion. Value children's ideas and help them to develop their ideas further

● allow the children to be in charge and to explain what they want before you intervene

● be positive — mathematics is fun!

Sean, aged 5, used the bricks provided in his nursery to build a tower. With encouragement, he drew a picture of his work, an activity which involved careful observation of shape

Be prepared!

We should play a very positive role in working mathematically with children. It helps if we:

● understand the mathematics the children are learning

● understand how children learn at this stage of their lives

● plan appropriate provision, activities, problems and challenges for groups and individuals

● observe children's responses and review planning in the light of these observations

The more we can do this, the better we will be able to make informed choices and take advantage of the opportunities available to each child. These are challenging areas in which we probably feel we never 'arrive' — however, small successes can come from simply developing and adjusting our current practice.

Talking with children about the maths they do is one of the most important things we can do to help them learn

Mathematical language

Mathematical language is an important part of children's learning of language generally. It is crucial to the development of thinking skills, and it allows children to talk precisely about their experiences, and to reflect upon them.

Aspects of mathematical language that need to be developed include:

Naming   Knowing the name of a shape allows children to talk precisely about shapes. Once a shape is named (for example, 'circle'), all the properties of the shape are drawn together in one word

Relationships   A lot of mathematical language describes relationships between shape, position, size and quantity (for example, 'shorter than', 'more than'). Without this language children cannot describe or explain these relationships

Questioning   When children become more accurate in their use of language, they will be able to express their curiosity by asking more probing questions (for example, "Why do the round ones roll better?")

Predicting and hypothesising   These are important mathematical processes. Children need to learn to answer questions such as "What would happen if we had ten biscuits?" and "Why do you think these blocks fit better?". They should be encouraged to ask questions, too.

What is mathematical language?

Mathematical language often involves:

● everyday words used in a precise and particular way. For example, a word like 'half' is often used to mean one of two parts that are *roughly* the same size. If used in a mathematical context it means one of two parts that are *exactly* the same size

● new words which are used only in mathematical contexts. Sometimes these are interchangeable — for example, 'subtract', 'minus' and 'take away'

What is the development?

In a mathematical context children will develop by:

● describing their mathematical experiences in their own words at first

● using an increasing variety of mathematical language

● describing and discussing mathematical properties and relationships more and more accurately

● offering explanations and posing questions in order to clarify and extend their ideas

Some children made models out of a collection of solid shapes. This 5-year-old drew a picture instead — of herself holding an icecream cone. The activity generated much talk about shapes

"Children use mathematical language, such as 'circle', 'in front of', 'bigger than' and 'more', to describe shape, position, size and quantity"

What to provide

● situations where children have to describe and explain mathematical relationships and problems (for example, "Say what you can feel in the feely bag")

● problems that challenge them both verbally and intellectually — "Shut your eyes and I'll change something. Now open them. What's changed?"

Things to say

● encourage children to talk about their experiences and listen to each other

● offer more precise ways of saying the same thing (for example, by rephrasing 'a round' as 'a circle')

● extend what children have said in slightly different words to show that there is often more than one way of saying the same thing (for example, "So you've shared these out – have you got the same number?")

Questions to ask

● "How could you describe what's in the feely bag?"

● "Can you tell me in a different way?"

● "Is there another way of describing it?"

● "What's the difference between . . ?"

● "How are they different? How are they the same?"

● "Do you mean . . ?"

● "Can you tell . . . what you have told me?"

● "Which brick did you choose to go on top? Why did you choose it?"

As part of a topic on Circles, the teacher drew each child a circle and asked them to turn it into a picture. Obi, aged 5, drew a bicycle. Talking to the teacher while he drew, Obi used mathematical language such as 'round', 'circle', 'straight' and 'next to'

What to look for

Does the child:

● talk about their mathematical experiences?

● provide a running commentary to their actions?

● invent words for ideas they don't know the language for? (for example, 'pointy bit' for corner; 'twenty-ten' for thirty)

● predict what may happen in mathematical explorations? (for example, "I think the big bear will make the scales go right down")

● hypothesise about mathematical ideas? (for example, "If we have more they won't fit in")

Developing some mathematics: circles

Children learn about circles as part of exploring shape and space. The circle is a good starting point for investigating similarities and differences in shapes.

What is the mathematics?

Young children can explore the ideas that:

● a circle can be made by pinning a string to a piece of paper, attaching the other end to a pencil, and 'walking' the pencil round

● circles can be of different sizes

● not everything that is curved is a circle

● the language associated with circles includes words such as 'round', 'curved', 'line', 'turning', 'rolling', 'rotating' . . .

● circles can be sorted from other shapes by distinguishing the properties of shapes, such as straight and curved lines, and sides and corners

What is the development?

Children develop by:

● recognising circles by sight and feel

● distinguishing circles from other shapes, beginning with contrasting shapes such as squares or leaves, and progressing to similar shapes such as ovals

● describing what they see and feel using a widening range of vocabulary to describe properties of shapes

● drawing and making circles

One 5-year-old's response to "How many little circles can you fit inside this big one?"

A circles game in the Reception class

What to provide

● games and activities in which children can physically make a circle — in movement, dance, using hoops, standing in groups of different numbers, pacing circles, drawing circles in the air, etc.

● songs, rhymes and stories involving circles

● a collection of circles — tins, lids, wheels . . .

● opportunities to explore circles in the environment — road signs, windows . . .

● opportunities to make circles — biscuits, pizzas, circles out of plasticine, printed circles, tessellated circles, drawn and painted circles . . .

● shapes to sort into 'circles' and 'not quite circles'

Things to say

"Can you collect all the circles from the box of shapes?"

"What can you say about your shape?"

"Which of these shapes go together?"

A 4-year-old's drawing of the circle game

Making circles in the Reception class

What to look for

Does the child:

● choose round shapes when they need things to roll, or to fit into a curved space?

● identify circles by name in pictures?

● make and use circles in cooking, patterns, games and on the computer?

● use words such as 'round', 'curved' or 'straight' appropriately?

● sort circles from other shapes?

Recognising patterns

Pattern is fundamental to mathematics. Exploring pattern gives a sense of regularity, which children will need later on in order to understand and recognise mathematical rules, solve mathematical problems and make generalisations.

What is the mathematics?

When they make patterns, children are learning to apply rules.

● when they make repeated patterns, children are forming sequences by repeating blocks of colour, shape, number, sound, or movement

● when they make growing patterns, they are applying the same rule again and again to form an increasing or decreasing sequence. (for example, singing 'Five Currant Buns')

● when making symmetrical patterns children are reflecting and rotating shapes

What is the development?

Children will develop by:

● intuitively making spatial patterns

● recognising, copying, extending and creating patterns which become more complex with experience

● discussing their patterns with an increasing range of vocabulary

● progressing from simple alternating patterns to sequences of *repeated* patterns. For example,

red, blue, red, blue

develops into a more complex pattern such as

red, blue, green, red, blue, green

or

red, red, blue, red, red, blue

● making sequences of *repeated* patterns in more than one direction (across, and up and down). These may be symmetrical, radial or 'surrounding' patterns.

● making *growth* patterns (where the same rule is used each time to change the shape or number), which are a stage on from repeated patterns. Children may try making a pattern grow by one more each time (for example, staircases with one more brick for each step)

● moving on from 'splodge patterns' to symmetry patterns by folding and cutting patterns

The patterns associated with eating meals can help children understand the idea of 'pattern' — each place setting is the same, the main course is always followed by the pudding . . .

What to provide

● a collection of simple patterned fabrics, wallpapers and wrapping papers from different cultures

● coloured bricks and beads

● counters, acorns and buttons

● coloured paper, scissors, mirrors

● ideas for the children to form patterns within the group (sitting, standing, sitting, standing . . .)

● musical and clapping patterns, movement and dance actions, songs and rhymes involving pattern

● paints and felt-tipped pens

● blocks and potato cuts for printing

Things to say

Look at and talk about particular patterns:

"What comes next?"

"Can you tell me why you chose a curly shape?"

"What could you make if you used yellow as well?"

"How has it changed?"

"Where does the next blue one come?"

Cover up an element in a pattern and ask "What have I hidden? How did you guess?"

A 4-year-old child represented sound patterns using circles and lines. The patterns were: 'drum triangle, drum triangle' and 'drum drum triangle, drum drum triangle'.

What to look for

Does the child:

● describe a pattern?

● copy it and extend it?

● create a pattern with a rule?

● make a more complex pattern than the previous one?

● make or continue a sequence pattern that goes in more than one direction?

● recognise, extend and create a growth pattern?

● make and explain simple symmetry patterns? (for example, make a Duplo model of an aeroplane where the wings are designed and placed symmetrically)

Rhymes, songs, stories . . .

Rhymes, songs, stories and games appeal to young children. They link home and school experiences, and provide an unpressured and social way of learning about numbers and counting.

These activities engage children through language, music, movement and the rhythm of repetition. Involving children in such multisensory and social experiences helps them to remember the numbers involved.

What is the mathematics?

Children are learning:

● the order of number names, forwards and backwards

● to count groups of things

● to count movements and sounds

● informal adding and subtracting, and counting in groups, using prompts such as fingers

● to recognise numerals

● to recognise the numbers of spots on a dice

What is the development?

Songs and stories which are introduced early on in the life of a group can be replaced by more sophisticated ones, involving more demanding mathematics.

An individual number rhyme such as 'Five Little Speckled Frogs' can be developed to get children:

● predicting the next number, then counting the number of frogs left

● putting numerals up on an easel to match the number of frogs

● increasing the number of frogs and having two frogs or more jump at a time

Stories can be extended by using props, and by asking children to predict (for example, "How many toys has Kipper got left in the toybox?")

Similarly, number games can be extended by:

● increasing the numbers involved

● using a numeral dice instead of a spotted one (and numerals on a dice could go up as high as ten)

● providing paper and easel or chalkboard for children to record scores

"They are familiar with number rhymes, songs, stories, counting games and activities"

What to provide

Provide appealing props which involve the children and allow them to retell stories and rhymes, such as:

- puppets, hats or masks

- toys, such as animals to put into the ark in twos

- miniature food items to go in a shopping basket

- green bottles pegged up on a line

- magnet board pictures of currant buns sold and money collected

- relevant props in the play area, such as five frogs in the water tray, or three billy goats with the large blocks

- tapes of stories and rhymes for children to listen to independently

- numerals to hold up, peg up on a line, or stick to a magnet board

Games and activities

- track games

- dice games involving the collection of objects

- number puzzles

- outdoor games involving tracks and shapes to jump on and count

- outdoor games involving skittles, beanbags, hoops and balls

- different methods of scoring games, such as easels, chalk, clipboards and large numerals

Things to say

Pose questions which encourage children to predict, visualise and think ahead:

"What do you think will happen next?"

"Suppose *two* frogs jumped off the log instead of one. What then?"

"How many more do you need to finish the game?"

"Whose turn is it next?"

"What do we do now?"

Children may need support when playing games, especially while waiting for turns. One way to provide this is to direct their attention to what others are doing:

"Krystel has thrown a six, but can't find a card with six on. Can anyone help her?"

"What number does Adaze want next?"

Older children can play games independently in pairs.

What to look for

Does the child:

- participate in activities and pay attention to the numbers?

- use counting spontaneously? Check their counting?

- read numerals on a dice or number track?

- make sensible predictions? (for example, predicting higher or lower number appropriately)

- keep the right number of tally marks, or write the correct numeral, to match a score?

13

Sorting

This section deals separately with sorting (this page) and comparing, matching, ordering and sequencing (pp. 16 and 17).

Children sort as part of learning about the world.

Children do not need to learn to sort before they understand numbers, as was once thought. However, sorting and categorising are important mathematical processes which children need to practise. Children can sort mathematically, for instance, by sorting shapes when tidying up, or by sorting numbers into odd and even.

What is the mathematics?

Children can learn to:

● sort objects by consistent criteria (for example, collecting all the things with holes in)

● sort objects by mathematical criteria (for example, sorting blocks by shape or by size)

● sort as part of data-handling (for example, deciding categories for sorting hats in the hat shop by size or by colour; including ladders on toy fire engines or construction toys as well as the bigger ladders used outside, and possibly the window cleaner's ladder)

What is the development?

● progressing from sorting with a changing criterion ('that one because it's shiny, and that one because it's big') to sorting based on a fixed criterion ('all the teddies')

● moving from subjective sorting ('the beads that I like') to sorting based on properties of the objects themselves ('the red beads')

● making finer distinctions (for example, moving from collecting 'all the big things' to collecting 'all the shapes with three corners')

● progressing into the abstract (for example, moving from sorting objects to sorting numbers)

● learning to sort and resort a set of objects using a different criterion (for example, sorting a collection of jewellery by size, then resorting by type)

● beginning to work with objects that could go into either one of two different sets (such as a large brick which could go with the big equipment or the building blocks)

Sorting out things which are attracted to a magnet

What to provide

● a variety of everyday objects for sorting — buttons, nuts and bolts, seeds and leaves — which will present them with the real problems we all face in sorting: Is this button really red or should it go in a new category called 'orange'? Does this seed count as a helicopter or not?

● plenty of interesting material for construction and model-making which will stimulate children to do informal sorting by shape and size

● sets of mathematical objects such as shapes and numerals

● opportunities to tidy up, or to set up a new role-play area such as a shop, which encourages discussion about sorting and ordering options (for example, sorting grocery packets by shape and size or coins according to value)

Children are engaging in sorting when they collect things from a known place, and when they put them back again at the end of play

Things to say

Encourage children to give reasons for their arrangements:

"How can we arrange the books so we know where to find the one we want?"

"Can you find any more like this one? . . . How are they the same?"

"Can you think of another way to sort the blocks?"

"Tell me why you chose *those* things"

"Can you see why I have put all these things together? Can you add some more to my set?"

What to look for

Does the child:

● use criteria consistently when sorting? (for example, when making groups of straight and curved blocks)

● give reasons for their sorting? (for example, "Those hats are all floppy")

● finish one sort then resort using a different criterion? (for example, arrange hats by size, then by shape)

Comparing, matching . . .

These processes help children make sense of their world and their place in it. Children make use of them naturally when telling stories, painting and music making.

Comparing, matching, ordering and sequencing are important mathematical processes. An understanding of them will help later on with mathematical ideas such as: comparing shapes and discussing their differences; sequencing events in the day; matching parcels that weigh the same; ordering numbers.

What is the mathematics?

Children can learn to:

● compare and visually match shapes and numbers

● compare and match things by informal criteria ("These ones look the same" "This is prettier than that one")

● compare and match things mathematically (by weight, size, length, area, volume and capacity, time . . .)

● put things in order (for example, putting Goldilocks' three bears in order of size)

● use one-to-one matching in order to find out whether or not two sets have the same number of items

● put things into a known sequence (for example, deciding what comes first, what comes next, and what comes last in the sequence of the day's events)

What is the development?

Children will develop in the following areas:

● *accuracy:* making fine distinctions when comparing things — for instance, two things that are close together in length. Children will begin by using vague words such as 'big' and little', then, helped by an adult's purposeful use of language, will refine these to words like 'taller', 'shorter', and so on

● *prediction:* being able to predict accurately (for example, which doll will fit into the toy bed)

● *abstraction:* using more abstract quantities (for example, comparing the weights of objects as distinct from size, or comparing abstract numbers)

● *complexity:* dealing with more items (for example, when putting things in order)

● *numeracy:* counting in order to compare numbers of things (for example, counting people to see how many cups are needed, rather than matching one-to-one); and counting in order to compare when measuring (for example, comparing heights using big bricks)

Acting out the events of a story in sequence

16

What to provide

● a variety of everyday objects for matching, comparing, ordering and sequencing, such as nesting dolls, cutlery and play people

● sand and water, and many different containers

● plenty of interesting material for construction and model-making. This will stimulate children into informal comparing: "This one's bigger" "I want a slopey one" "This one's the same"

● mathematical equipment such as shapes and numerals for children to put in order or find the matching pair

● stories involving sequencing, supported by props (toys, or magnetic or feltboard pictures) for telling the story in the right order

Things to say

Offer children words like 'shorter', 'taller', 'wider', 'narrower', 'deeper', 'holds more than'.

"Do you think that will fit in there?"

"Which has more?"

"Can you tell me why you think that?"

"Can you make a taller tower?"

"Can you make the scales balance?"

"What goes on first? . . . Does it matter what you put on next?"

What to look for

Does the child:

● use comparative vocabulary? (for example, say 'tall' or 'high' rather than just 'big')

● make statements using 'than'? (for example, "This is curlier than that")

● make fine comparisons between things that are not very different? (for example, "This cup's got more sand in than that one")

● predict and deal with imaginary comparisons? (for example, "When Titch gets bigger, the clothes will be too small")

● compare in terms of weight? (for example, saying that the little tin of beans is heavier that the big cereal packet)

● use one-to-one matching in order to find out whether two sets have the same number of items and comment to that effect? (for example, "There aren't enough cups")

● use counting in order to decide whether or not two sets have the same number of items?

● put into order three or more things (for example, order three bears by height), then find where an extra item fits into the order?

● sequence several items, using words such as 'first', 'second' and 'last'?

Counting

This statement has been dealt with in three separate parts. The first part covers cardinal and ordinal numbers, and counting. The second part, Larger Numbers, *deals with numbers as labels. The final section,* Reading Numbers, *concerns recognising written numbers.*

What is the mathematics?

Numbers can be used in three ways:

● as labels (for example, on a front door or a bus). This is called 'nominal'.

● to indicate how many items there are in a count (for example, on the notice "There are 15 houses on this model"). This is called 'cardinal'.

● to indicate when something is in order (for example, "The office is the third door along". This is called 'ordinal'.

This section deals with the latter two: cardinal numbers and ordinal numbers. The next section, 'Larger numbers', deals with nominal numbers.

What is the development?

It is not possible to count without knowing some number names, so learning these must come first. The order in which children learn other counting skills may vary but the progression might be:

● learning the first few number names in the right order, perhaps followed by other numbers in random order ('1, 2, 3, 6, 7, 13 . . .')

● saying one number for each item counted, without missing any or counting an item more than once (helpful activities at this stage are jumping games, throwing beanbags, counting people by touching them, and moving objects)

● understanding that the last number you say tells you how many there are (it is helpful at this stage to count the same items in a different order many times)

● getting a feel for estimating quantities by looking at the pattern of objects, such as the dots on a dice (arranging small numbers of objects in different ways and looking at the patterns, playing dice games with large dice, and collecting objects and arranging them are all helpful activities)

● learning more number names in order and being able to say what number comes next without going back to one again

● using rhymes and stories to count backwards from 5 to 0

● using ordinal number names such as 'first', 'second' and 'third'

Counting steps along the walkway

"They recognise and use numbers to 10 and are familiar with larger numbers from their everyday lives"

What to provide

Opportunities for counting in daily activity:

● tidying up: counting the aprons, the paintbrushes, the pictures . . .

● rhymes and stories that include number sequences such as '1, 2, 3, 4, 5, Once I Caught a Fish Alive'

● action games and rhymes, throwing and jumping and clapping games, using hands and feet as much as possible

● counting the children themselves

● counting repetitive sounds and beats on percussion instruments

● playing board games and counting games

Opportunities for using ordinal number words such as 'first' and 'second':

● queuing

● signing up to use the computer

● sequencing events in the day

● thinking about the processes of cooking, planting, getting dressed . . .

Singing a song involving numbers

Things to say

Encourage children to re-count a collection of objects or people from different starting points. Ask them to predict, then count, in order to develop estimation skills.

"How many biscuits are there? Are there enough for everyone?"

"How do you know how many you've got?"

"Hide by the time I have counted to 9 and I will come and find you."

"I am thinking of a number. When you count, it's next after 2. What is it?"

"Who will be first to reach me? Who will be second?"

What to look for

Does the child:

● say the numbers in order?

● say one name for one object, without missing any out, or counting any twice?

● organise counting — keeping track of ones already counted, separating them from those not yet counted?

● say the last number when asked how many?

● say what number comes after 5 without re-counting?

● check counting by using a different starting point?

● use the words 'first', 'second' and 'last' correctly?

Larger numbers

At the nursery stage, children are beginning to grapple with different uses for numbers, and should be comfortable with smaller numbers to 5, 10 or 20. When children meet numbers larger than those they readily understand, they will tend to see them all as 'labels'.

So why should young children learn about numbers that they will not, for the time being, use for counting? The answer is that children need to learn about larger numbers because they meet them in everyday life, and young children are often interested in larger numbers.

What is the mathematics?

As well as learning the first few numbers, to 5 or 10, children are aware of all sorts of larger number names. Besides numbers for buses and houses they may know ages for people in their family, telephone numbers, times for television programmes, such as 'four-thirty', and so on.

What is the development?

Children may arrive in the nursery knowing all sorts of things about larger numbers, and some may even know about counting in a language other than English. We can draw on this knowledge in discussions and activities, and help children to make connections between what they already know and what they are learning.

Progression may be in:

● extending known sequences, like '7, 8, 9' or '51, 52, 53'

● using the pattern of teen numbers as a chant — thir*teen*, four*teen*, fif*teen* (or maybe three*teen*, four*teen*, five*teen*)

● collecting and sharing knowledge of large numbers such as 'a million', or 'the 73 bus'.

Toy telephones provide an opportunity for children to meet larger numbers

"They recognise and use numbers to 10 and are familiar with larger numbers from their everyday lives"

What to provide

● rhymes, rhythmic chants, songs and stories with number sequences

● opportunities for children to share and compare their knowledge of numbers

● large numbers on carpet tiles, large number lines, large number grids to show numbers in a sequence

● everyday discussions about numbers as labels (for example, "These shoes have got a size 28 on them")

● discussions about higher number values (for example, "When we're all here, there are 32 children. At the pancake party there were more than a hundred of us.")

● calculators to show large numbers

Things to say

Use the counting sequence in as many different contexts as possible. Encourage children to predict the next number in the sequence.

"What numbers do you know? Do you know any big numbers?"

"What is the biggest number you know?"

"How old are you? How old do you think I am? How old is your nan?"

"The number on my front door is 54. Do you know the number on yours?"

"13, 14, 15, . . . Can you guess the next number?"

"Tell me what phone number you are going to dial"

This 5-year-old wanted to count the books on the shelf, then to record her work without adult help

What to look for

Does the child:

● join in the chanting of number sequences over 10?

● continue a sequence over 10 independently?

● talk about large numbers they know? (for example, tell you the number of a house or a bus, or the age of their big brother)

● remember a sequence of numbers such as a telephone number?

Reading numbers

See also *Recording Numbers,* pp. 26 and 27.

Children want to learn about reading numbers because these are part of their everyday world. They come across written and printed numbers in their everyday lives on birthday cards, microwave ovens, lottery cards, televisions, and so on.

What is the mathematics?

As we have seen, numerals can be used in three ways: as labels; to indicate a number of items; and to indicate a position in a sequence.

We need to ensure that children experience numbers in all three ways.

What is the development?

Young children learn to read numerals that mean something to them, such as birthday cards and badges, or door numbers.

They eventually need to be able to:

● distinguish numbers from letters

● recognise and name the digits 0 to 9 in a variety of styles

● put these digits in order

● understand that a numeral can indicate how many things there are (for example, that there are six eggs in the eggbox)

● read numbers in a range of contexts (recipe cards, page numbers, price labels, clothes sizes . . .)

Children enjoy 'helping' with reading books, so make sure you have plenty of books that contain numbers, and the children will learn to recognise them without effort

"They recognise and use numbers to 10 and are familiar with larger numbers from their everyday lives"

What to provide

Ensure that numbers occur in the nursery environment as frequently as possible. Make sure that children see numbers written in different ways. Help them to understand when numerals are used to indicate how many of something there are.

You could provide resources to enable children's development in the following areas:

● *technology* videos, microwaves, clocks and watches, computers, calculators and tape recorders. Discuss numerals with children, particularly the different ways in which a number can be written

● *measuring equipment* tape measures, scales, measuring cylinders, clocks, watches and calendars

● *tactile numbers* wooden, raised, dough, feely or card. Make a collection of, say, 4s, and ask children to sort them out and to notice all the variations

● *children's familiar numbers* birthday cards, telephone numbers, door numbers, shoe sizes, labels on clothes. Include numerals in scripts from different cultures

● *numbers in order* large floor and wall number grids, floor number lines, large number tiles and number friezes

● *environment* a number walk, experience of shopping and dealing with coins, or 'collecting' numbers outside. Encourage children to guess why numerals occur where they do in the environment, and what they are for. Collect labels from packages

● *organisation* labels to show how many children can play in an area, stock-check labels for equipment and games

● *games and puzzles* jigsaws, board games, dominoes with numerals, number lotto

● *books* counting books, telephone directories, catalogues, almanacs, stories involving numbers, recipe books and cards

Things to say

"What is that number?

"Can you find:

— the number that shows your age?"

— all the numbers in your family?"

— the number that shows how many fingers you have?"

— the number that shows how many conkers we have collected?"

— the number after this one?"

— your door number?"

— your telephone number?"

— the number that goes with the rhyme?""

— your sister's/brother's age on the number frieze?"

"Can you put these numbers in order, then read them?"

"Which numbers look like other numbers in some way?" (for example, 3s and 5s, 2s and 5s, 6s and 9s . . .)

"Why is that number there?" (for example, on a road sign)

What to look for

Does the child:

● point out numbers on signs, and distinguish numbers from letters?

● read the number 4 written in a variety of styles?

● pick out the correct number when it is upside down and back to front?

● understand when a number indicates to you how many things there are?

● put some numerals in order, such as 1, 2 and 3?

Solving problems

Everyday problems can offer children interesting and enjoyable challenges, particularly when the problems are their own. Children might experience problems such as: making sure everyone, including themselves, gets a biscuit; getting dressed; seeing who has won a game.

Children learn about mathematics when trying to solve problems. It is helpful to talk about different approaches to solving the same problem. For example, children can experiment with and discuss different ways of tackling a jigsaw puzzle, or of packing the blocks back in the box, identifying and sharing key strategies such as where to start.

What is the mathematics?

Solving practical problems can involve children in many aspects of mathematics:

● comparing, sorting and matching

● counting

● adding and subtracting (and even, sometimes, multiplying and dividing)

● classifying shapes

● measurement

Being involved in the process of problem–solving also gives children the skills needed to:

● tackle a problem

● relate the problem to others they've solved (for example, using fingers to show how many biscuits have been eaten)

● use the mathematics they know (for example, recognising that square corners fit together)

● devise short-cut methods, such as counting to lay the table instead of dealing out plates one at a time

● estimate sharing out (for example, where there are 12 sweets between 3 teddies, deciding that there are enough to give the teddies 2 each the first time round)

● behave as mathematicians, suggesting the use of rulers, weighing scales, calculators, and so on, as appropriate to solving problems (although they may not know how to use them or precisely what they are for)

What is the development?

Children will begin to:

● use more sophisticated strategies (for example, starting to fit some of the flat surfaces together instead of piling blocks randomly in the box)

● develop their mathematical skills and knowledge (using numbers to record a score in a game rather than tallies)

● be more thorough and systematic (for example, counting the story prop hats and moving them to one side as they are counted, or counting to check that the right number of items has been collected in a collecting game)

● make more informed choices about the methods they use, and explain why they chose that method (for example, saying they chose the corner the pieces of a jigsaw puzzle first because they're easier to find)

● solve harder problems, in unfamiliar contexts (for example, sharing 12 sweets between 3 teddies, then re-distributing them evenly when another teddy comes along)

"They begin to use their developing mathematical understanding to solve problems"

What to provide

Children need a variety of contexts in which they can engage in exploring, playing, making, and posing their own mathematical problems. These contexts could include:

● construction and creative activities

● mathematical games

● routine preparation and setting up

● planning special events like parties

● decision-making and voting (for example, deciding a name for the guinea-pig)

● sharing food, cooking and tidying up

● posing problems in role–play or small world play, and asking questions arising from stories

Things to say

Nothing at first. Just listen to, and observe, the children.

Later, acknowledge and respond to children's questions and comments. Turn their comments around to form questions:

Calum It won't fit in.

Teacher Why won't it fit in?

Calum 'Cos it's too fat.

Teacher What can you do?

Calum Turn it round.

If the children get 'stuck' or need help, ask open questions, such as:

"What have you thought of so far?"

"What could you use to help you?"

"Have you seen something like this before?"

At the end of the task, recap with the children the whole problem-solving process, using appropriate mathematical language.

What to look for

Does the child:

● show signs of having a plan? (for example, collecting the blocks they need before they start building)

● explain the methods they use? (for example, putting blocks lengthways to make a taller tower)

● show signs of being systematic and organised? (for example, checking all the trikes are in the parking bays with their matching numbers)

● use mathematical knowledge and skill? (for example, reading the number on a recipe card to see how many spoons of flour are needed, or finding the numeral they want on the computer keyboard by counting along from 1)

● extend their reasoning to solve more complex problems? (for example, can they deal with 10 speckled frogs instead of 5, or predict how many would be left if 2 jumped off at a time?)

● suggest using a mathematical tool? (for example, offering a tape measure to solve the problem of moving the computer into a smaller space)

Recording numbers

Children learn best about recording numbers in practical situations where they understand the purpose of what is being counted. This helps them see how the number symbols are used, and to understand what they mean.

What is the mathematics?

Numbers can be used in three ways:

● as labels (for example, on a front door or a bus). This is called 'nominal'.

● to indicate how many items there are in a count (for example, on the notice "There are 15 houses on this model"). This is called 'cardinal'.

● to indicate when something is in order (for example, "The office is the third door along"). This is called 'ordinal'.

What is the development?

Children will develop by:

● using their fingers to represent numbers

● recording numbers using 'tallies' and then progressing to the use of numerals

● using a series of numerals for one number, for example, using '123' to represent 3. This is a common middle stage.

● recording numbers by selecting a wooden or plastic numerals

● knowing what numbers look like, and which numerals to write

● writing well-formed and legible numerals

Note: children may still be reversing numbers when they are 6 or 7 years old — this is quite normal.

Old typewriters allow children to make marks on paper which they can begin to recognise and name: this is an important step towards making their own meaningful marks

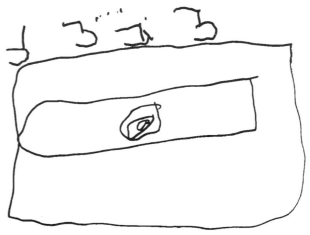

This 4¹/₂-year-old counted the number of nesting shapes he had drawn and made several attempts at writing the number 5 as a record. Recording numbers usually involves the child in using numerals, as in this example. However, children can also record using tally marks

> *"Through practical activities children understand and record numbers, begin to show awareness of number operations, such as addition and subtraction, and begin to use the language involved"*

What to provide:

● numerals, in a variety of forms, indoors and out, for children to select and handle

● a number line, chart, or 100-square, with other number apparatus for reference

● plastic or wooden numerals to use as props when singing number rhymes with actions (for example, 'Five Little Frogs' or 'Ten Fat Sausages'), or playing games such as skittles

● number and counting books

● numbers in a variety of scripts, such as Bengali

● opportunities to write numbers in different ways (using tallying or a 'personal numeral system')

● opportunities to keep scores for games, such as throwing bean bags in buckets

● labels for shop items

● blank labels on boxes the children have filled

● personal number books (containing, for example, numbers of people in their family, ages, door and telephone numbers)

● reasons to communicate and remember numbers

Jade, aged 3¹/₂, was playing a game with floor shapes. She jumped onto two shapes and recorded her jumps with these marks, explaining it by saying "One, two, four, six". Clearly she has the idea that you can record jumps on paper, but has not yet got the idea of matching one tally mark to one jump

Things to say

Help children to understand the importance of written numbers by talking about them in the situations where they occur.

If children want to record mathematical activities, do it in the same way as shared writing: children can offer their own suggestions for recording numbers, and the adult can demonstrate standard ways of doing this. The children can then try out the suggestions they have shared (including other children's ideas) and standard forms.

"Can you show us how many there will be?"

"Can you find a number to tell us how many skittles have fallen over?"

"Can you find the number on the calculator?"

What to look for

Does the child:

● use tallies or numerals to represent amounts?

● write several numerals for one amount (for example, writing 123, or 333, for three) showing they know the numerals but not how they are used?

● know when to use, and how to write, zero?

● choose a numeral from a collection to record a number situation?

● press the right key on the calculator when asked to press 'the five' or 'the seven'?

● write legible numerals?

Addition and subtraction

What is the mathematics?

Addition   Various words are used to talk about addition, such as 'more than' and 'altogether', depending on the situation . We need to help children see what is the same about these terms, and understand that the different words all refer to the same idea of combining two numbers.

Subtraction   There are two main kinds of subtraction, 'taking away' and 'how many more' type problems. Children can solve practical subtraction problems in all sorts of ways. For instance, you might say to children "There are only two people so far who want to make playdough, and we could have six, so how many more can choose to do this?" Children might work it out by 'regrouping' six fingers into 2 and 4, or they could add on from 2 to 6 or they might just 'know' that 4 and 2 makes 6.

What is the development?

Children will show progress by:

● combining two lots of objects, and finding the total, or removing some objects, and counting the number left

● solving imaginary problems set in familiar contexts (for example, "If the tiger and lion came to tea too, how many people would there be?")

● adding 1 or 2 to, or subtracting it from, a number

● predicting results before they can see the answer ("I think it'll be 5")

● solving problems where one group of things is hidden (for example, "There were 5 beads, but I hid some. You can see there are 3 left — how many did I hide?")

● knowing some number bonds, such as '2 and 2 makes 4'

● talking precisely about what they are doing

● tackling problems with bigger numbers

A note about sums   Children may be familiar with '+' and '−' signs from home, and may happily play at using these signs and symbols before they understand how to use them properly. However, even when children can do 'sums' by using counters, and can write them down using '+' and '−' signs, this does not mean that they are able to solve other addition or subtraction problems. This can mislead parents into thinking children are able to do addition when they are really just counting.

Children need opportunities to develop their own ways of doing addition and subtraction. This will increase their confidence and their understanding far better than concentrating on 'sums'.

Cooking provides many opportunities for addition — for example, "One more spoonful" or "Two more buns"

"Through practical activities children understand and record numbers, begin to show awareness of number operations, such as addition and subtraction, and begin to use the language involved"

What to provide

Young children enjoy solving problems in the context of games. One puzzle-like game that they enjoy is the box game. You need a box with, say, five bricks in it. Children should be able to see how many bricks are put in the box (perhaps putting them in themselves) and how many are added to, or subtracted from, the bricks in the box — but not the contents of the box. They try and guess (or work out) how many are in the box at the end of the operation.

This game can be adapted by using different objects, and can be played with a group. With several children, ask them to represent their guess by holding up fingers, or (for older children) using a number card.

Other things to provide are:

● sweets or toys to share in situations where some must be added or taken away to ensure everyone has the same

● singing rhymes where the predicted sequence is altered (for example, when singing 'Ten Fat Sausages', two or three go 'Pop')

● scoring facilities for outdoor and indoor games

Things to say

It is important to use a range of language for addition and subtraction, so that children realise that different words express the same idea: 'together makes', 'not enough', 'the same', 'take away', 'more (than)', 'fewer (than)', 'difference'. Use questions which encourage children to think and predict, such as:

"Have you got more than . . ?"

"Have you got less than (or fewer than) . . ?"

"How many do you think there will be?"

"Can you tell me how you did that?" (Be prepared for the child to be unable to offer an explanation)

Offer a range of language to do with counting, such as 'more than', 'fewer than', 'lots', 'many', 'too many', 'too few', 'not enough', 'how many?'.

What to look for

Does the child:

● combine two lots of objects, put them together and say how many there are?

● add 1 or 2 to (or subtract it from) a number in the context of a rhyme or game?

● predict results before they can see the actual answer ("I think it'll be 5")?

● use the language of addition and subtraction, talking about 'how many there are altogether' or 'how many there are left'?

● solve a problem such as "There are 5 bugs in the box and 2 have escaped. How many are left?"

● spontaneously tell you things like "2 and 2 make 4"?

Useful number rhymes

Songs with 'two' and 'three'

TWO LITTLE EYES

Two little eyes to look around,
Two little ears to hear each sound;
One little nose to smell what's sweet,
One little mouth that likes to eat.

ALSO

Baa Baa Black Sheep

I Saw Three Ships

Counting forwards

HICKETY, RICKETY, RUMPETY

Hickety, rickety, rumpety, ricket honicup,
How many fingers do I hold up?
You said one.
I've just begun.
You said two.
One for me and one for you.

ALSO

I Have a Little Chiming Clock

On the First Day of Christmas

Once Upon a Time in a Nursery Rhyme

One Elephant Went Out to Play, on a
Spider's Web One Day

One Man Went to Mow

One Potato, Two Potato,
Three Potato, Four . . .

Once I Caught a Fish Alive

One, Two, Buckle My Shoe

Peter Hammers with One Hammer

This Old Man

When Goldilocks Came to the House
of the Bears

Counting backwards

FIVE LITTLE DUCKS

Five little ducks went swimming one day,
Over the pond and far away.
Mother Duck said, 'quack, quack, quack,
quack'
But only four little ducks came back.

Four little ducks went swimming one
day, etc.

ALSO

Two Little Dicky Birds

Five Little Buns in the Baker's Shop

Five Little Frogs Sitting by a Well

Five Little Men in a Flying Saucer

Five Little Monkeys

A Tall Silver Rocket

Ten Little Seagulls

Ten Little Speckled Frogs

Ten Fat Sausages

There Were Ten in the Bed

Ten Green Teddy Bears

Addition and counting in groups

Open the Oven

Open the oven.
It's very hot.
Put in the loaves.
In they pop.
Four on the bottom,
And six on top.

How many loaves altogether?

(the numbers can be varied each time)

ALSO

I Went Fishing

One and One are Two

Swinging on a Gate

Five Little Ladies

Twenty Red Skittles

Ching Tou Leng Fly the Kite

Subtraction

My Twenty Coloured Handkerchieves

My twenty coloured handkerchieves
Are hanging on the line.
How many of them must I take
In order to leave nine?

(the starting number can be varied each time)

ALSO

Clucket Cluck

A Fat Green Crocodile

Fifteen Little Apples

Others

Five Little Peas

Five little peas
In a pea pod pressed.
One grew, two grew,
And so did all the rest.
They grew and they grew
And they did not stop
Until one day
The pod went 'pop'.

ALSO

Bluebells, Cockle Shells

Here's the Beehive

Useful Books

Many of these songs and rhymes can be
found in one or other of the following books:

Talking Points in Mathematics

Anita Straker, Cambridge University Press
1993, ISBN 0 521 44785 5

This Little Puffin

Elizabeth Matterson and Claudio Munoz
eds, Puffin 1996, ISBN 0 1403 4048 3

	Comparing, sorting and matching (including measuring)	Counting and recognising numbers
Progression (the maths)	Sorting collections using mathematical terms (numbers, shapes and sizes) Comparing length, weight, capacity, area, time, or things which can be counted Making finer distinctions, dealing with a greater number of things or properties, moving from real objects to possibilities: "If we had . . ."	Saying numbers in sequence Counting things saying one number name for each object Knowing last number indicates how many things there are Reading numerals Guessing (estimating) how many
Practical contexts	Planning and preparing parties, picnics (real and pretend), involving surveys . . . Sorting out and tidying up in the context of block play, home corner, construction toys, role play, outdoor play . . . Playing Dominoes, Pairs, Memory Game Sorting and classifying interesting collections of objects Wrapping up presents Growing things: mung bean sprouts, amaryllis Comparing: which holds more? (using boxes, bottles, jugs . . .) Seeing who can build the tallest tower Dressing up and dressing dolls Outdoor activities: obstacle race	Checking the number of children in a group Counting for their own purposes Counting in a variety of contexts: music, ball games, printing . . . Acting out number rhymes with props Collecting numerals in the environment: buses, houses, shoe shop, clinic . . . Role play: rocket, hairdresser, post office . . . Making their own equipment for role play: washing machine, aeroplane cockpit . . . Dice games and other counting games Making up and adapting their own games
Pattern seeking	Using ideas of 'the same' and 'different' to sort and classify patterns Talking about the language patterns when counting: thir*teen*, four*teen*, . . . twen*ty*, thir*ty*, . . . Using sequences: the order of putting on clothes, the order of adding ingredients in cooking . . . Using size in describing and designing patterns	Recognising and using number in repetitive patterns: in outside play (2 little jumps, 1 big jump, 2 little jumps . . .); in music, dance, clapping rhymes; in art and design (3 squares, 2 circles, 3 squares . . .); in pegboard patterns . . . Recognising and using the step pattern in counting:
Language	same, different, more, less, fewer, both, and, is, is not, belong, have, haven't, does, does not, too much, too little, long (-er, -er than, -est, enough) tall, short, heavy, light, full, empty, wide, narrow, fast, slow, covers (area), balances, before, after, times of day and of year . . .	zero, one, two, three . . . ; first, second, third . . . ; more, fewer, more than, fewer than, lots, many, too many, too few, not enough, how many?, count
Resources	Collections of interesting everyday objects: feathers, screws, keyrings . . . Sets of objects that are the same, similar, different Different sized objects: containers, zips . . . Different shaped objects: buttons, shells . . . Everyday sets around nursery: construction sets, dressing-up clothes, exploring kits . . . Different tools: tape measures, timers, clocks, calendars, scale, balances, thermometers, callipers, spoons, jugs . . . Sand and water, small beads, beans or lentils for filling Construction toys for comparison of sizes Different games: Memory, Lotto . . .	Anything countable, in any context, including the children themselves Local environment: shopping, cooking . . . Role play: shop, café, clinic . . . Snack time Number line, pegboards, dice games, Bingo, beads, bricks and blocks, number puzzles Calculator, computer, programmable toys such as Pip and Roamer, toy phone, cooking timer
Books and rhymes	Such as: *Elmer; How Do I Put it On?; Titch; Bad-Tempered Ladybird; Giant Jam Sandwich; Jim and the Beanstalk*	Such as: *The Doorbell Rang; The Very Hungry Caterpillar; The Cockatoo Book*
Children's recording	Photography, paper strips for comparison, plastic numerals to record number of non-standard units . . .	Practising numeral shapes in sand, with paint, chalk, pencil . . . Child's own mark-making, tallying, leading on to use of standard numerals

Beginning to solve number problems	Exploring shape and space
Combining numbers or objects (addition) Comparing numbers or objects (more than/less than) Taking away numbers or objects (subtraction) Beginning to work with greater confidence, larger numbers and more complicated situations, such as sharing	Recognising a variety of 2D and 3D shapes in different places Using a variety of 2D and 3D shapes in various ways Recognising and using position words Transferring ideas learnt in one situation to another situation Using and recognising a greater variety of shapes Using position words with greater accuracy
Collecting and spending games Counting for their own purposes: How many different grasses have we found? How many more biscuits do we need? Becoming familiar with the calculator Adding and subtracting in story contexts and role play situations: shop, bus, jumble sale . . . Cutting up sandwiches: what shapes, how many pieces? Sharing out food, toys, equipment . . .	Making things for their own purposes: envelopes, kites Building castles, boats, houses and planes for imaginative play Constructing things, and in the process planning, predicting, making, testing, discussing, solving problems Altering, adjusting and extending constructions and models Creating pictures, collages, patterns and designs Discussing and playing with large apparatus and toy vehicles Playing games such as 'Guess My Shape', posting shapes, feely bags, nesting boxes Tidying up, putting things away according to shape codes, packing things into boxes
Working with two groups of objects (for example, red and yellow eggs), what different ways can we arrange them (in the egg box)?; similarly for two types of biscuits on a plate, or two kinds of animal in a stable that holds five animals	Recognising symmetrical patterns in the environment: leaves, flowers, doors . . . Creating symmetrical patterns in a variety of media: paint, printing, magnetic tiles, children's own bodies . . . Recognising and creating patterns using lines and shapes, again in the environment (fabrics, wrapping paper . . .) Designing patterns for their own purposes Using positional and descriptive language to plan, predict, test, discuss patterns in the environment and their own patterns
how many, how many more/fewer?, difference, each, sharing, equals, altogether, take away (in context), add, subtract, count on, count back	next to, beside, before, after, turn around, rotate, turn over, reflect, under, on top of, forwards, backwards, round, flat, straight, curvy, line, corner, angle, roll, slide, stack, pile, fit, don't fit, 2D, circle, triangle, rectangle, square, 3D, cube, cuboid, sphere, pyramid, cone, repeat, continue
As for number Pip and Roamer — 3 lengths and 2 lengths more	Big blocks (wood and plastic), Quadro, crates, Duplo, Lego, Multilink, PolyM, Meccano, Community Playthings attribute blocks, construction straws, wet sand, playdough, clay, plasticine, paint, collage, junk modelling, fuzzy felt, road mats, vehicles, outside play, tunnels, snack time, pegboards, pinboards.
Such as: *Katie Morag; Red Riding Hood; Kipper's Toy Box*; 'Five Little Ducks'; 'Five Currant Buns'; 'Ten Little Monkeys' . . .	Such as: *The Patchwork Quilt; Bears in the Night; Rosie's Walk; Inside, Outside, Upside Down; We're Going on a Bear Hunt; A Witch Got on at Paddington Station*
Drawing and tallying (for example, a bead necklace) Making an explanatory picture and writing about it (with an adult as scribe) . . .	Recording with photos, telling about it, making models and display Mark-making (drawing or writing) about it, with adult as scribe where necessary Drawing plans, and writing labels for games such as Hops

Activities table

The table on the previous two pages contains a detailed breakdown of the mathematics involved in the 'desirable outcomes' and ways in which they can be interpreted.

Along the top are four areas of mathematics, grouped in ways that we as adults find helpful — in reality children's experiences are not always so distinct. Down the left-hand side are listed categories that we consider worthwhile in planning mathematical activities for children. The activities are not all intended to be adult-led; many will arise out of the day-to-day activities of the nursery. The aim is to observe children, support what they are doing, and extend their activities and thinking in suitable ways: *observe, support, extend*.

The suggestions offered are exactly that — suggestions. You will recognise some and have lots of others to add to the list once you begin to follow the children's interests.

In order to develop children's mathematical learning in a curriculum where they can learn from first-hand experiences in their play, the teacher/adult's planning and specific use of mathematical language is of the greatest importance.